WHAT PEOPLE ARE SAYING

MW00619957

"Important and exciting! I Like Giving could be the beginning of a movement of generosity."
—MARK BATTERSON, author of *The Circle Maker*

"I Like Giving will light you up on the generosity dial."
—DAVE RAMSEY, host of "The Dave Ramsey Show" and New York Times best-selling author

"I Like Giving inspires us to explore giving that is full of cheer and joy. These stories have opened up our eyes to see our daily interactions with people in a whole new way."
—DAVID AND BARBARA GREEN, cofounders of Hobby Lobby

"Brad's understanding of generosity is a wake-up call for the giver inside us all."
—MICHAEL JR., award-winning comedian

"I Like Giving is a beautifully written book with the right title, because people really do like giving. Brad Formsma has an inspiring message, and his book should be on every kitchen table, like a daily vitamin for the soul."
—STEPHEN POST, best-selling author of *Why Good Things Happen to Good People*

PARTICIPANT'S GUIDE

I LIKE GIVING

THE SMALL GROUP EXPERIENCE

PARTICIPANT'S GUIDE

I LIKE GIVING

THE SMALL GROUP EXPERIENCE

BRAD FORMSMA

I Like Giving Participant's Guide

Copyright © 2017 by Brad Formsma

Published by I Like Giving

Details and names in some anecdotes and stories have been changed to protect the identities of the people involved.

Cover design by Baas Creative

Printed in the United States of America
2015 First Edition, 2017 Revised Edition

ISBN: 9780692482285

PARTICIPANT'S GUIDE

I LIKE GIVING

THE SMALL GROUP EXPERIENCE

CONTENTS

USING THIS GUIDE

This participant's guide is designed to be used along with the book I Like Giving. All of the videos referenced in this guide can be found at this site: http://ilikegiving.com/experience-videos

We have divided the guide into four sessions that walk you through the journey of living generously, beginning with the spark that inspires you to give, moving to the change it effects in you personally, then to the impact it has on your family, friends, and community, and finally to the difference it can make in the world.

I want this study to provide you with an experience, so it was designed to feature a mix of activities to do in a group setting or individually, including stories, videos, and discussion questions.

At I Like Giving, we're all about helping you discover the joy of generosity. Jesus, the greatest teacher, once said, "It is more blessed to give than to receive," and I believe that is true. I trust that you'll find greater meaning and joy as you begin to experience the life that is truly life.

Brad

I Like Giving Participant's Guide

Session 1: Awareness

DISCOVERING THE JOY OF GIVING

PREPARATION

For this session, read chapters 1, 2, and 3 of *I Like Giving*. Access the videos for this session at: http://ilikegiving.com/experience-videos

PART I: THE POWER OF ONE GIFT

For many of us, giving may seem like a no-brainer. It's just the right thing to do. However, most of us struggle with giving on some level. Maybe it's because you feel you don't have anything to give. Perhaps you feel overwhelmed by the need and don't know where to start. It could be that you've just been so busy living your life that you haven't noticed of the needs around you.

It's okay. You are not alone. But, I want to help you figure out a way around whatever obstacles stand in the way of giving because living generously is a practice that changes the lives of everyone involved. One simple act of generosity can reach far beyond what you touch in your daily life.

Section I is about bringing awareness. Too often, we just aren't aware of the needs all around us, or have no idea how easy it can be to make a difference. In Part I we will explore what can happen when we decide to give just one gift and begin to understand the chain reaction it can set off.

READ: "I LIKE HOLIDAY INN EXPRESS"

Bill from Michigan:
Upon checking into my hotel, Holiday Inn Express, I noticed a family, a mother and four children, ages five to fifteen, sitting in the lobby. What got my attention was that two of the older

children were actually reading books as opposed to playing video games on their phones. And all of the children were very well mannered. (It's sad in this day and age that this is unusual behavior and is what captured my attention.)

After I completed check-in, I heard the mother talking on the phone. She had no money for a room or food. I had just heard the sermon at my church, Vineyard North, on Sunday regarding I Like Giving and realized I could help. I had extra money.

I went to the desk clerk, paid for their room, and gave the clerk $200 in an envelope to help them through the next couple of days. I included a message explaining that I fully believed God put me there at the right time and made me sensitive to their need.

The desk clerk later told me the family was overwhelmed at the generosity. He said the mother was a Christian and began to cry, thanking God that He had heard her prayers. I felt overwhelmed that God blessed me with this opportunity to help! I cannot even get to sleep tonight as I am on such an emotional high!

WATCH

Video #1- "I LIKE LISTENING"

REFLECT

DISCUSS

1) In Ch. 1, you read the story of Tracy who received a timely gift of Thanksgiving dinner. She was not in a position where we would expect her to give, but this one gift had such an impact on her that it changed her life and her perspective on giving. Do you recall your first giving experience? How did it start? What prompted you to give?

2) It's a normal human response to want to know that our generosity made a difference—that it wasn't wasted effort. Think of the first time you expressed your generosity. Do you feel it made a difference for you and for the other person? How did you feel afterward? How do you think the other person felt?

3) The point of living generously is to begin impacting the world around us in the hope that it will stretch farther than we can reach on our own. What do you think would happen if every person on the planet began looking for ways to give? How do you think it would change the world if everyone chose to live generously?

PART II: BEGINNINGS

Those who've had positive experiences with generosity indulge in it regularly. But many people have had negative experiences that left them feeling skeptical and guarded. Perhaps someone took advantage of their generosity and it left them feeling disheartened. Sometimes people just end up feeling discouraged because they don't see results from their giving that make it seem worthwhile.

My hope as we begin this journey into a more joyful and generous life is to start by exploring how we got here, by wrestling with our own stories in order to understand how we got to this place. I hope to point a way forward for you to a liberating, vital life of joy fueled by generosity. I have found that generosity isn't something you ever master. Instead, it's something that masters you. The deeper you go, the more joy, beauty, and goodness you find.

READ: "WHEN IT'S YOUR IDEA"

Brad Formsma:

Several weeks ago my son and I stopped at FedEx to have some documents printed. The woman behind the counter was in the middle of a large project. "This is going to take a few hours," she said. "Maybe you'd like to come back later?" she suggested. I was thinking, "Maybe you'd like to take thirty seconds and print my documents!" But, I bit my tongue and we agreed to come back after dinner.

A few hours later, my son and I headed back. As we were walking in, the woman we'd spoken with earlier was walking to her car. She smiled and let us know our project was done and that she'd done it herself, but now she was headed off for dinner.

Then I felt it. The nudge. I thought I should buy her dinner, but immediately my brain began to rationalize why that would be weird. We walked a few more steps when my son Drew squeezed my hand and said, "Dad, I think we should buy her dinner." So we spun around and did just that.

Twenty-four hours later, our family was eating together at Chick-fil-A when a woman approached our table and asked for money to buy something to eat. I fumbled in my pocket for some money and gave it to her. When she walked away, my family's silence was palpable. "Okay," I said. "You think I just got taken?" We laughed at the pregnant silence and then had a great conversation about it.

But the difference between what happened at FedEx and Chick-fil-A is significant: one was our idea, the other wasn't. Paul says, "Each of you should give what you have decided in your heart to give." When giving is your idea, it's powerful.

I don't have the generous life figured out by any stretch of the imagination, but I'm convinced we're made for generosity. It's not something we do here or there from time to time. It's what we are. It's what we're made for. So in every situation we are called to be just that, whatever that may look like. We can't let one or two bad experiences rob us of the joy we were made for.

WATCH

Video #2 - "MR. SKEPTIC"

REFLECT

DISCUSS

1)   Brad responded to the skepticism of his family by being willing to give in spite of the possibility that someone might take advantage of him. But, this was after building a life of generosity. It isn't always easy to have that attitude when you are getting started. What experiences have you had that shaped how you think about generosity and giving? Are you skeptical? Is generosity something you think of as a duty or an obligation?

2)   In Ch. 2, Brad tells the story of how his grandfather influenced his desire for giving, but he talks about feeling burned out by that sense of duty later on. If you or someone you know has had a negative experience with giving, what response did you have? Did you stop giving or change your approach? How might you practice generosity in a way that helps you see it in a positive light?

3)   Whether it's well-meaning parents trying to instill good values in us or charities needing support for their causes, it is easy to feel like everyone wants something from us and end up with donation fatigue. Has someone ever "guilted" you into giving? How did that make you feel? Was there a time when giving was your idea that had a different outcome?

PART III: TRY

One of the most common barriers to the generous life is the assumption that generosity means giving money. There are endless ways to be generous, and part of the joy is discovering what we have to offer. In the story of the feeding of the five thousand, the disciples see a need and ask Jesus to do something about it. Jesus sees the same need and asks the disciples to do something about it. They begin freaking out immediately: "That would take more than half a year's wages!" But then Jesus asks a simple question: "How many loaves do you have?"

Jesus isn't interested in what they don't have. He's interested in what they do have. He also asks this question of us—one that echoes through the ages: "What do you have?"

Not long ago I heard the true story about a group of onlookers who rushed into the smoking wreckage of a car accident to rescue someone who was trapped. They dragged the passenger to safety just moments before the car burst into flames. What's remarkable about stories like this is how consistently the heroes say, "I didn't do anything special. I was just there. I saw something needed to be done, and I did what anyone else in that situation would have done."

Here's the thing: miraculous and heroic things happen through ordinary people responding to what they see, where they're at, with what they have at their disposal. When we respond to what's in front of us with what we do have—whether that's money, a smile, or a listening ear—God is pleased to transform the ordinary into the extraordinary. The generous life is far more about availability than it is capability. I like to say that Jesus was highly interruptible. Nothing He was up to seemed so important that He couldn't take a moment to be fully present to those around Him—and Jesus was up to some pretty important stuff!

READ

"I LIKE FLAGLADY" (from Ch. 3 in *I Like Giving*)

WATCH

Video #3 - "I LIKE BUGSHELLS"

REFLECT

_____

_____

_____

_____

DISCUSS

1)   As rewarding as giving is, if it becomes an obligation, we don't receive the joy from it that we should. The point of giving is to feel you are making a difference. What might you need to change about your attitude regarding giving to find the joy in it again? Do you need to change your perspective about what giving entails?

_____

_____

_____

_____

2)   Giving takes shape in lots of ways we don't even consider. It can be in the form of our time, our gifts, or our funds. What are some things you've been doing in your life that have helped others that you may not have thought of as giving? What personal gifts do you have to offer that can be a part of living generously without breaking the bank?

_____

_____

_____

_____

3)   Living generously means looking for ways to be selfless, to do something for someone else that does not benefit you other than by giving you that "warm, fuzzy" feeling. What steps can you take to begin looking for those opportunities to be generous daily? What is one way you can train your mind to be open to the possibilities?

_____

_____

_____

_____

LIVE IT

Hopefully by now you're catching on to the explosive joy available to us when we give, a joy that—if we let it—could totally transform our lives and the world. I believe we were made to give. I believe giving is an extremely potent, redemptive force, and because of that, I also believe it's one of the things the Enemy wants to prevent us from doing. So it should come as no surprise that the minute we consider living generously, we're confronted with a whole host of objections:

"I'm too busy."
"They don't really need my help."
"I don't have anything to give."
"I'm only giving because I'm supposed to."
"Am I enabling people by helping them?"
"I'll be in a much better place to be generous once."
"What if they use my gift to buy drugs?"
"It feels awkward."

It is important to understand that the generous life can get derailed before the train even leaves the station. When we start talking more about our fears, uncertainties, and suspicions about the misuse or abuse of our generosity, the Enemy has won. He's gotten us off the transformative journey into the generous heart of God and into the weeds where we're more likely to get stuck. That's not to say we shouldn't be wise about how we give. That's not to say that being generous won't be messy sometimes. All of those things are true. But we can't let these barriers keep us from living the life God made us for. My hope is that each of us can identify and acknowledge the barriers that keep us from the generous life and then enter into the complexity, finding fresh energy and imagination from God as we overcome those barriers and step into the joy we were made for.

CONSIDER

Read the passages below at home for further exploration and contemplation.

When Jesus landed and saw a large crowd, he had compassion on them, because they were like sheep without a shepherd. So he began teaching them many things.

By this time it was late in the day, so his disciples came to him. "This is a remote place," they said, "and it's already very late. Send the people away so that they can go to the surrounding countryside and villages and buy themselves something to eat."

But he answered, "You give them something to eat."

They said to him, "That would take more than half a year's wages! Are we to go and spend that much on bread and give it to them to eat?"

"How many loaves do you have?" he asked. "Go and see."

When they found out, they said, "Five—and two fish."

Then Jesus directed them to have all the people sit down in groups on the green grass. So they sat down in groups of hundreds and fifties. Taking the five loaves and the two fish and looking up to heaven, he gave thanks and broke the loaves. Then he gave them to his disciples to distribute to the people. He also divided the two fish among them all. They all ate and were satisfied, and the disciples picked up twelve basketfuls of broken pieces of bread and fish. The number of the men who had eaten was five thousand. (Mark 6:34–44, NIV)

Remember this: Whoever sows sparingly will also reap

sparingly, and whoever sows generously will also reap generously. Each of you should give what you have decided in your heart to give, not reluctantly or under compulsion, for God loves a cheerful giver. And God is able to bless you abundantly, so that in all things at all times, having all that you need, you will abound in every good work. As it is written:

"They have freely scattered their gifts to the poor; their righteousness endures forever."

Now he who supplies seed to the sower and bread for food will also supply and increase your store of seed and will enlarge the harvest of your righteousness. You will be enriched in every way so that you can be generous on every occasion, and through us your generosity will result in thanksgiving to God. (2 Corinthians 9: 6–11, NIV)

There are three things in these Bible passages that we should pay close attention to. Paul stresses we should purpose in our own hearts what to give, rather than giving under compulsion or out of a sense of obligation.

Next, Paul goes on to say there's a mystery at work in the generous life. Conventional wisdom says that when you give, what you have is diminished or depleted. But, according to Paul, whoever sows sparingly reaps sparingly and whoever sows abundantly reaps abundantly. As we give, our lives aren't diminished and depleted; they are enriched. Paul suggests that living into this mystery should give us the confidence and readiness to be "generous on every occasion."

Every occasion? Really? Even if I don't feel like the people need my generosity? Even if it seems like I have nothing to give? Even if it feels awkward? Even if I'm concerned my giving might be abused? The answer is yes. Paul says, "On every occasion."

ACT

Watch for opportunities to be generous in small, nonfinancial ways:

- fold someone's laundry,
- be attentive to whoever is speaking to you,
- make time for others around you.

Use the journal pages in the back to write about your experience and come to the next session ready to discuss what you did and how it felt to do it.

I Like Giving Participant's Guide

Session 2: Decision

REDEFINING GENEROSITY

PREPARATION

Read chapters 4-7 of *I Like Giving*.
Access the videos for this session at:
http://ilikegiving.com/experience-videos

PART I: WHAT HAPPENS WHEN WE GIVE

In the last session we explored the inspiration for giving—what ignites a desire in you to want to give—and what it means to live a life of generosity. You were challenged to look for small, non-financial ways to give to someone else. Use the next few minutes for the group to share their experiences and thoughts.

Once you've had an opportunity to share, think about what experiences you had in common. Do you recognize any similar themes in your experiences? While each giving opportunity has its own unique details and outcomes, the impact on the life of the giver and the receiver is fundamentally the same. It is important to remember that giving is not just about doing something for others. Sometimes we need to give more than other people need to receive. There is science to show that we experience real, physiological changes when we give. Research shows that giving to others can make us happier and healthier. In this part of the session, we will explore what happens when we give.

READ: "I LIKE LAUNDRY"

Lexie from Michigan:
I am a student at the University of Michigan. Like most college

students, I have many tasks to complete on a given day. As a result, I am often distracted and fail to remember to complete the little chores in life, such as laundry.

Last Friday afternoon I noticed that the stack of clothes coming out of my laundry bin was growing quite high. I gathered all my dirty bright-colored clothing in a bin and put them into the washing machine. Soon after putting my laundry in the machine, I forgot all about it.

The next morning I woke up in a panic. Immediately I realized I had totally forgotten to transfer my clothes from the washer to the dryer. I ran downstairs to the laundry room, scared that someone may have stolen my clothing or thrown my clean clothing on the dirty laundry floor. But instead of finding my clothing in bad condition, I discovered that all of it had been dried, then neatly folded, placed carefully in grocery bags. On top of the bags was a note that read, "Dear fellow resident, I hope I made your day a little better :) Sincerely, Anonymous."

I was so stunned that someone would be kind enough to take time out of their busy schedule just to do another student's laundry (not to mention pay the cost to run the dryer). This act of kindness made my day. I will be sure to "give it forward."

WATCH

Video #4 - "I LIKE CAR"

REFLECT

DISCUSS

1) In the story "I LIKE CAR," we heard about two acts of giving, one prompted by the other. What did you note about the experiences of the two givers? Have you ever felt the same way?

2) Catherine sacrificially gave everything she had saved to someone who she felt was in greater need than she was. In the moment she responded to a need without any second thought, but later wondered if she had made a mistake in giving so much. How would you respond to Catherine's question? Have you ever regretted being generous? If so, how did things work out in the end?

_____

_____

_____

_____

3) At the end, Debbie says, "Generosity begets generosity." Do you agree with that? Do you think Catherine's willingness to be give without reservation opened her up to greater blessings? How do you think this experience changed each person involved?

_____

_____

_____

_____

READ: "I LIKE IMMIGRATION"

From a former student:

After nearly seven years of graduate school, the end was finally in sight. It had been a long, hard slog, working full-time, parenting two small children, and taking a full load of classes. All that remained between me and graduation was a cross-cultural immersion experience. I shuddered at the thought of it. I'd been on loads of cross-cultural experiences. I'd been to Thailand and had seen firsthand the sex trafficking of women and children. I wasn't exactly thrilled to be away from my family for what was sure to be a lame, Cross-Cultural 101 experience. What happened there changed how I understand my life and those of others around me.

We were studying immigration along the US/Mexico border in Arizona's Sonoran Desert, but we were also serving meals and listening to people's stories. Soon we were in Nogales meeting migrants who'd just been deported. I shared a meal with a man who couldn't afford to buy protection from the cartel after he'd been deported. His face was freshly bruised from where he'd been beaten and robbed. He'd hung drywall in Nashville for twelve years. "Good work," he smiled. "No cracks."

Everyone we met had a story of finding a body in the desert. I met a woman named Shura who has devoted her retirement to walking the desert in search of migrants who've gotten lost and need water and medical attention. Shura is General Patton in the tiny frame of a sixty-year-old woman.

The more people I met, the more I felt my heart opening to the world around me in a strange way. I became aware of the fact that I'd been living my life totally focused on my own struggles. It wasn't a particularly joyful life either.

But here, as I opened myself to the struggles, aches, and

needs of the people around me and responded, my heart was coming alive. I began wondering, "What is it about responding to the struggle and the suffering of another person that makes me feel alive?" I left the border a different person.

These days, when I'm in a funk, I ask myself: "Where is the struggle in the lives of people around me?" That's where the joy of giving is.

WATCH

Video #5 - "THE SCIENCE OF GIVING"

REFLECT

DISCUSS

1) According to research, spending money on ourselves does not improve our happiness the way spending money on others does. Think about the last time you bought something simple, such as lunch, for yourself and think about a time you bought lunch for someone else. Do you recall feeling differently about them? What differences did you experience?

2) Stephen Post identified ten ways of giving: celebration, generativity (helping others grow), forgiveness, courage, humor, respect, compassion, loyalty, listening, and creativity. Most of these don't even have to involve spending money. Do you think people would live more generously if they could view giving in these terms instead? How do these ways of giving change your desire to live more generously?

3)   This participant's guide is structured to take you through the steps of discovering the desire to give to understanding how it impacts you and the world around you. How have you seen generosity changing you?

_____

_____

_____

_____

PART II: GIVING FILTERS

Even though we may understand the importance of giving and get a good feeling when we do it, there are a number of excuses people give themselves for why they don't follow through on that nudge to give when it comes up. Some people convince themselves they don't really have the time or money to give. Others avoid giving because they've had a bad experience in the past—maybe someone took advantage of them, was not grateful, or rejected their generosity. But, one of the most common reasons people give for not acting on a need is that they feel overwhelmed and fear they won't make a difference. The needs are too great and beyond their abilities.

It is important to remember that our job is not to save the world. As Catherine said in the "I LIKE CAR" video, you cannot give what you do not have. But, you can give what you do have, and most of the time that is enough. The willingness to give starts a chain reaction that stretches far enough to touch the lives of people you don't believe you can reach. Just start where you can with what you have and don't forget that giving takes a lot of forms.

READ

"I LIKE HEAD LICE" (from Ch. 6 in *I Like Giving*)

WATCH

Video #6 – "I LIKE BEING 98"

REFLECT

DISCUSS

1) Evelyn had a number of limitations that could have prevented her from living generously. We might gladly give her a pass since she is 98! But she didn't allow herself to use that as an excuse, saying, "I'm on the earth! I'm here! If I can contribute, I should. Shouldn't we all?" If you were in Evelyn's shoes, would you still look for ways to give? How does she inspire you to look for opportunities in spite of your own limitations?

2) Evelyn's contribution was simply getting her driver's license and driving her neighbor to the store, and yet her story has stirred millions of people. Why do you think such simple acts of generosity are so profoundly meaningful?

3) The great thing about Evelyn's story is in how her desire to help not only made a difference for her neighbor, it gave her new purpose at a time in her life when most people are treated as useless. What are some ways that giving could help you find a new direction or purpose for your life? Share how you have experienced this in your own life.

_____

_____

_____

_____

PART III: GIVING TACTICS

Once you have the desire to life a life of generosity and are working past the limitations that have prevented you from acting, it can still be tough to get started. You may not know how to find opportunities or you may be unsure about the best way to address a need.

Ch. 7 outlines helpful tactics for approaching giving under challenging circumstances. For example, you may find it necessary to give discreetly or anonymously and not receive any acknowledgement for your actions. That can be tough, but it is important to remember that you don't have to receive thanks for generosity to change another person's life and to change your heart. The story "I LIKE WATER HEATERS" is a great example of this.

READ

"I LIKE WATER HEATERS" (from Ch. 7 in *I Like Giving*)

WATCH

Video #7 – "I LIKE LAUGHTER"

REFLECT

DISCUSS

1)   In "I LIKE LAUGHTER" Michael Jr. explains that everything changed for him when he saw his comedy as an opportunity to give something to his audience instead of trying to get something from them. How might this same attitude affect the way you view giving? Could this extend to other areas of your life as well? In your job? In how you relate to your spouse or children?

2) Michael Jr. explained that he realized his calling was to make laughter commonplace in uncommon places. By shifting his focus, he found a new direction and a new purpose, just like Evelyn did. What can you learn from both of these stories about how generosity might make a difference in how you live?

3) We have read and heard a number of stories sharing remarkable and unconventional ways of looking at giving. How have these examples changed your view of what giving looks like and what it means to live generously?

LIVE IT

In our consumer society, we constantly find ourselves in settings where our sole reason for being there is to *get*. We go to the supermarket to *get* groceries. We go to the coffee shop to *get* coffee. We go to a restaurant to *get* a meal. We go to the gas station to *get* gas.

Think about all of the times throughout your day when you might have an opportunity to "flip the script" and *give* instead. Maybe it's buying coffee for the person in line behind you. It could mean staying a little later at work to help someone finish a task. Or, it might be as simple as doing the dishes when it's not your turn. Living generously is about looking at every aspect of your life as an opportunity to get outside yourself and do for someone else.

CONSIDER

Command those who are rich in this present world not to be arrogant nor to put their hope in wealth, which is so uncertain, but to put their hope in God, who richly provides us with everything for our enjoyment. Command them to do good, to be rich in good deeds, and to be generous and willing to share. In this way they will lay up treasure for themselves as a firm foundation for the coming age, so that they may take hold of the life that is truly life. (1 Timothy 6:17–19, NIV)

If you have any encouragement from being united with Christ, if any comfort from his love, if any fellowship with the Spirit, if any tenderness and compassion, then make my joy complete by being like-minded, having the same love, being

one in spirit and purpose. Do nothing out of selfish ambition or vain conceit, but in humility consider others better than yourselves. Each of you should look not only to your own interests, but also to the interests of others.
Your attitude should be the same as that of Christ Jesus:
Who, being in very nature God,
did not consider equality with God something to be grasped, but made himself nothing,
taking the very nature of a servant, being made in human likeness. (Philippians 2:1–7, NIV)

Jesus devoted most of His Sermon on the Mount to what might be called "transforming initiatives." He addressed things like anger, lust, vengeance, and money to show how conventional religious wisdom traps us in a false piety. Just because you don't murder someone doesn't make you holy. If you're murdering that person in your mind or with your words, you're guilty.

Jesus offered a transforming initiative to learn to live in the freedom of the kingdom of God: go and be reconciled. To live in this kingdom requires a totally new mind. It means we're going to have to start pursuing a new mindset on lots of things, including generosity.

ACT

Use the list of ten ways of giving from Stephen Post and see if you can fit one of each into your life this week.
- Celebration
- Generativity (helping others grow)
- Forgiveness
- Courage

- Humor
- Respect
- Compassion
- Loyalty
- Listening
- Creativity

Use the journal pages in the back to write about your experience and come to the next session ready to discuss what you did and how it felt to do it.

I Like Giving Participant's Guide

Session 3: Impact

BUILDING A CULTURE OF GENEROSITY

PREPARATION

Read chapters 8, 9, and 10 of *I Like Giving*.
Access the videos for this session at:
http://ilikegiving.com/experience-videos

PART I: FAMILY

In session 2 we discussed the impact that giving has on us as individuals and looked at the science of giving—how the act of generosity can have a physiological effect on us. You were challenged to use Stephen Post's list of ten ways to give and try to fit one of each into your life during the week. Use the next few minutes for the group to share their experiences and thoughts.

Recently I was at a meeting where someone posed the question "How many of you learned to be generous from a parent or grandparent?" Every hand in the room except one went up. Generosity is much more caught than taught, which is why modeling generosity, especially for kids, is so important. For my wife and me, maybe the most joyful part of our journey into the generous life has been watching the impact it's had on our children. We decided early on not to obligate or pressure them into giving, but it was clear the stories starting to bubble up from our own experiments were making an impact on them. So we started presenting possibilities to them.

Our kids were eager to be generous. They just needed permission, and I think that's true for many people. They have a desire to live generously but don't know how or where to start. I'm convinced that's why generosity is so contagious, because whenever someone starts being a blessing and living generously, it lights the way for others to join in. It gives them permission. It presents them with a possibility. Our faithful, generous presence—wherever God has put us—lights a path for others to follow.

READ: "I LIKE FUNERALS"

Brad:

My education in generosity began as a kid tagging along with my grandpa on Saturdays. In the first chapter of I Like Giving, I wrote about how he showed me a list of organizations he gave to and how much joy it brought him. The joy he derived from being generous left a huge mark on my life. Many, many years later, at his funeral, I was standing next to his casket saying goodbye. It turned out he had one last lesson to teach me.

As I stood there processing my emotions, a man came up next to me. After a few moments, he began telling me the story about how his wife had died tragically several years ago. He had been completely devastated. "Your grandpa," he told me, "heard about our situation and paid for her funeral."

You can probably imagine the surge of both sadness and joy that shot through me at that moment. In both life and death, my grandpa was modeling the generous life for me. It was so moving. I sensed it was much more than a great story. It was an inheritance, a heritage to carry forward.

WATCH

Video #8 - "I LIKE QUARTERS"

REFLECT

DISCUSS

1)   Giving the bikes was a family gift, but Laura was reluctant to put too much effort into it thinking it would be a wasted effort because she was sure someone had already met their need. What kind of impact did following through have on her giving mindset? What did the effort do for her family that was beneficial for them regardless of the outcome?

2)   We see in the way the kids respond that they have "caught the giving bug" and even went above and beyond to make sure they could follow through. What part of the experience of giving do you think resonated most with them?

_____

_____

_____

_____

3)   This act of generosity took a good bit of effort, but was well worth the extra time. What do you think it teaches their children about a life of giving that they overcame a number of obstacles to follow through?

_____

_____

_____

_____

PART II: COMMUNITY

Just as modeling generosity for our families can have a lasting, generational effect, giving can have a ripple effect that stretches through our communities, our workplaces, and even the world. In fact, we may never know just how far-reaching our single act of giving can be or how lasting the effects will be. Generosity is for all of us.

Let's take a moment and consider that: Generosity is for all of us. It strengthens relationships and builds community by opening our eyes to those around us. It also allows us to show our weaknesses and know others will help if they can. I dare you to test this theory and see just how much an impact you can have on your community by living generously.

READ

"I LIKE TRUMPETS" from (Ch. 9 in *I Like Giving*)

WATCH

Video #9 - "I LIKE BIKE"

REFLECT

DISCUSS

1) Brad and Laura are beginning to see the fruits of their efforts by modeling generosity for their children. Why do you think it's important for their family to learn to give willingly and without prompting?

2) When Brad started this activity with Drew and his friends, he did not have a giving opportunity in mind, but he and Laura had laid the groundwork for their children by modeling generosity. Have you done anything to instill a heart for giving in other members of your family? If so, how have you done that?

3) Brad did not recommend Drew put his money in the Giving Jar; Drew just did it on his own. And, he did not insist his friends put their money in the Giving Jar. He simply

modeled giving behavior and they followed his lead. Why do you think modeling giving behavior might encourage someone to give more willingly and more frequently than just telling them to give?

_____

_____

_____

_____

PART III: RECEIVING

Another aspect of impacting your family and community through generosity is learning how to receive well. Receiving is often harder than giving because it reminds us that we need other people. But isn't that what family and community is all about? Also, if you have been giving, then you know how much joy you experience through those acts. Remember, as we discussed in the last session, sometimes giving is more for you than for the recipient. Don't you think someone else deserves to feel that too? If you refuse a gift from someone, you may be denying them the opportunity to experience that same joy.

In order to become a good giver, it is important to become a good receiver as well. That might mean acknowledging your own limitations or vulnerabilities, but it will be rewarding in the long run for everyone involved.

READ

"I LIKE HAIRCUTS" (from Ch. 10 in *I Like Giving*)

WATCH

Video #10 – "I LIKE MILITARY"

REFLECT

DISCUSS

1) The members of our military give in ways many of us will never know about, much less comprehend. We thank them for their service when we see them in uniform, but how often do we consider the hardships their families can endure while they are away serving or when they return home? What are some needs you think they might have that are going unaddressed?

2)   The desire to serve your country is something all soldiers do with pride and it can be hard to accept gifts from others in gratitude for that service. What kind of impact do you think being able to receive had on this family?

3)   The generosity this military family received was a great surprise for them and very moving, but the giver also received something as well. What do you think this act of giving did for them? How would being able to give like this affect you?

LIVE IT

A single act of kindness can indeed trigger a wave of human goodness. Perhaps you've seen the bumper sticker "Practice random acts of kindness and senseless acts of beauty." This bumper sticker advice taps into the age-old wisdom that our actions, no matter how small, have the capacity to effect profound change. But what we are exploring is something far deeper than the temporary swell created by a single act of random kindness. Consider what happens when we—as Dallas Willard has written— "practice routinely purposeful kindnesses and intelligent acts of beauty." Identify someone for whom you'd like to model generosity (your child, a friend, business colleague, etc.), and present that person with an idea to join you in doing something generous this week. Partner together in carrying it out.

CONSIDER

In the same way, let your light shine before others, that they may see your good deeds and glorify your Father in heaven. (Matthew 5:16, NIV)

They devoted themselves to the apostles' teaching and to fellowship, to the breaking of bread and to prayer. Everyone was filled with awe at the many wonders and signs performed by the apostles. All the believers were together and had everything in common. They sold property and possessions to give to anyone who had need. Every day they continued to meet together in the temple courts. They broke bread in their homes and ate together with glad and sincere hearts, praising God and enjoying the favor of all the people. And the Lord added to their number daily those who were being saved. (Acts 2:42–47, NIV)

Generosity, when practiced routinely and purposefully, can shape and change cultures: family cultures, neighborhood cultures, work cultures, church cultures, and school cultures, and the list goes on. What I love about the Acts passage we read a moment ago is the way it shows what a culture of generosity can do to a community. These first Christians enjoyed the favor of all the people. Why? It seems their generous lifestyle had implications for the neighborhood. Whether you were a follower of Jesus or not, the faithful, generous presence of these people simply made the neighborhood a better place. Being a faithful, generous presence always has implications for those who happen to be nearby.

For many people, modeling generosity or sharing stories about generosity might seem to fly in the face of what Jesus taught. But in order to appreciate what Jesus was getting at, it's helpful to understand the religious culture in which He taught. Jesus lived and taught in the first century within a culture rooted in the dynamics of honor and shame. Honor was highly valued, and people sought to acquire honor in the eyes of others. What's more, the Old Testament commanded Jews to perform certain acts like fasting, prayer, giving to the poor, and observing certain codes of purity. These were deeds carried out for God. But in a culture that prized honor, suddenly these deeds were performed less for God and more for the eyes of others. This was exactly the kind of hypocrisy Jesus challenged. The problem wasn't that someone might see your good deeds. The problem was performing those deeds in order to be seen by others and win honor in their eyes.

Jesus was addressing the motive of the heart, which is why elsewhere in the Sermon on the Mount Jesus taught, "Let your light shine before others, that they may see your good deeds and glorify your Father in heaven" (Matthew 5:16, NIV). Whatever culture you find yourself in—a family culture, work culture, school culture, church culture, or neighborhood culture—know that your faithful, generous presence has life-giving implications for anyone who happens to be nearby.

ACT

Identify someone for whom you'd like to model generosity (your child, a friend, business colleague, etc.), and present that person with an opportunity to join you in doing something generous this week. Present the idea and invite them to partner together in carrying it out. You might even describe this group and assignment, and ask them to help you in doing it.

Use the journal pages in the back to write about your experience and come to the next session ready to discuss what you did and how it felt to do it.

Session 4: Action

TAKING GENEROSITY TO THE WORLD

PREPARATION

Read chapters 11 and 12 of *I Like Giving*.
Access the videos for this session at:
http://ilikegiving.com/experience-videos

PART I: BECOMING A GIFT

Session 3 focused on the impact our giving can have on others around us and how modeling generosity can change minds, hearts, and lives. You were challenged to get someone to partner with you in an act of generosity. What steps did you take to do that and what was the outcome? What did you learn about inspiring generosity in others?

When we practice giving of ourselves on a regular basis, we become a gift to everyone we encounter. Our lives are a gift to our communities and beyond when we open ourselves to the possibilities and respond to the nudges that come up. When we live generously, the actions we take also become a gift to us as they contribute to our personal growth and enrich our lives.

READ

"I LIKE PEACE" (from Ch. 11 in *I Like Giving*)

WATCH

Video #11 - "I LIKE ADOPTION"

REFLECT

DISCUSS

1) The Dennehy children were all treated as "rejects" because of their birth defects and other health challenges, yet the Dennehys chose them. It is easy to see how the parents have become a gift to these children, but in what ways are these children a gift for their parents as well?

2) Adoption is a gift in many ways even though it also presents challenges. When you add to them the extra consideration of special needs, it seems even more heroic. What do you think the Dennehys get out of taking in so many children with challenges that many would use as an excuse to pass over them? How would you respond to the nudge to take on such a huge responsibility?

---

3) Sometimes being a gift requires a great deal from us, maybe even unimaginable sacrifice. But, part of the message of I Like Giving is that living generously doesn't have to be that difficult. It does, however, require we respond to needs when we see them. How have you become attuned to opportunities for giving and being a gift to someone else as you've gone through this study?

PART II: A GENEROUS WORLD

It is easy to feel overwhelmed by the needs in our own communities, never mind the inconceivable volume we see around the world. It is tempting to back away and throw your hands up in frustration and ultimately do nothing. But that is not the right answer! Instead, we should be looking for opportunities to make whatever difference we can on our own where we are and look for others to partner with for having a greater impact.

It is impossible to fix everything that is wrong in the world on your own, but when we work together, we can accomplish the unimaginable.

READ: "I LIKE GIVING"

Brad:

A few weeks ago I was making a deposit at the bank. When the teller saw "I Like Giving" on the check, he asked what I did.

"I try to inspire people to be generous," I said.

"Nice," he replied. "Do you mean, like, to nonprofit organizations?"

"No," I answered. "Just being generous to anyone. Period."

He smiled and shrugged his shoulders. "Well, if you've got it, give it."

"We've all got something to give," I chirped back.

He paused for a moment, and then a look of surprise came over his face. "You're so right," he said. "Our world needs that."

Our world does need that. Our world—so full of anger, envy, and self-interest—desperately needs people who live according to a different script, people who refresh one another with a lifestyle of giving.

Often, when we think about impacting our world through generosity, we automatically assume that has to mean giving to nonprofit organizations doing work globally. While it is important to support those groups, creating a generous world doesn't have to be so huge in scope. Achieving a generous world starts right at home—your home, my home. We change the world by changing ourselves and then inspiring others to change as well.

I hope my story and the other stories I've shared with you have inspired you to begin living generously so you can join us in the ongoing work to make a generous world.

WATCH

Video #12 – "I LIKE SOCCER BALLS"

REFLECT

DISCUSS

1)   In visiting Mozambique, the family recognized that needs extend beyond just sustenance and shelter. Quality of life is important as well for us as human beings. How do you see hope being a factor in creating a generous world?

2)   At first it was hard to find someone to partner with their efforts, but eventually people responded to the generosity this young boy was modeling for them. The important take away is that he didn't give up. Have you let obstacles keep you from responding to a need you know you are supposed to address? If so, how might you overcome that in the future?

3)   One of the most poignant statements in the video was that generosity can change the way we see others and how we react to difficult situations. How do you see generosity having this kind of impact on our world? In what ways can seeing other differently help our world become more generous?

_____

_____

_____

_____

PART III: HOW WILL YOU LIVE GENEROUSLY?

Now that you know the impact giving can have on you, your immediate circle of influence, and even the rest of the world, you will begin to see opportunities arise to give. You've also learned that giving can take many forms and be done on many levels. You know that it doesn't have to involve a lot of time or money, though you can go above and beyond if you feel led to do so.

With all of this information and so many inspiring stories to guide you, how do you plan to proceed? How will you begin living generously? I hope, no matter how you go about it, that you at least will take that next step.

READ: "I LIKE THINKING AND DOING"

Brian from Tennessee:
Running is more than exercise for me, it's an opportunity for me to think—and lately I've had one particular thing rolling around my mind. I took off down a somewhat secluded trail behind my office. It curves around beneath an overpass. As I rounded the corner, it caught my attention. Tucked up high on the ledge near what would be the bottom of the road was a small Christmas tree with stockings hanging from it.

I can only assume it was a homeless person's way of keeping alive at least a sliver of the Christmas Spirit. It also unlocked for me the opportunity to do what I'd been thinking about so much. It was an opportunity to practice being generous.

Now, I've always considered myself a generous person, but the more I thought about it, I realized I'd been a generous person when opportunities found me, but that changed when I saw the film "I Like Adoption."

After seeing that, I knew I had to do something. I had to be more aggressively generous.

The video is a short story about a husband and wife who have adopted six children from all over the world, some of whom have significant disabilities. I was moved by the couple's unconditional spirit of giving, and it challenged me to openly look around for opportunities to be generous.

I wish I could say I went out and did something extravagant like adopt children with special needs to give them a safe, loving home, but I didn't. All I did was return to the overpass and leave a small amount of money and a note for a person I've yet to meet. I'm hoping in some small way he or she received it as an act of kindness that arrived in a moment of need.

I don't see it as "mission accomplished, generosity complete." I see it as a beginning. Seeing the couple's generosity inspired me to be more alert to what is going on around me and to do what I can to be generous.

So I've quit thinking about what I can do for others and started thinking about what I will do for others. The doing makes the thinking much more fun.

WATCH

Video #13 – "HOW WILL YOU LIVE GENEROUSLY?"

REFLECT

DISCUSS

1) As we discussed in the beginning, living generously becomes a way of life simply by making it a part of your life, by not passing up opportunities to give that present themselves to you. How do you intend to begin incorporating giving into your life as a result of participating in this study?

2) The reason giving feels so good is because we are made to be generous beings. Meeting needs of any sort does something affirming for us as individuals in addition to helping someone in need. What have you experienced as you've begun to live a life of generosity that compels you to keep going?

3) Living generously is also contagious. By modeling this behavior, your family, friends, co-workers, and other members of your community will begin to take notice and will likely look for ways to do the same. How can you engage those in your sphere of influence to join you in a life of generosity?

LIVE IT

Each session has closed with recommendations for how to apply the ideas covered. Since this is our final session, we won't be gathering together again to talk about your efforts during the week. It's time to implement everything we've discussed into your life and really LIVE IT. The members of your group may want to work on giving projects together. Or, if you have been working through this study on your own, you may want to find people in your sphere of influence who are willing to join you on this journey. I am excited for the ways your life is about to change and the doors you are opening to greater blessings.

CONSIDER

A generous man will prosper; he who refreshes others will himself be refreshed. (Proverbs 11:25, NIV)

Therefore everyone who hears these words of mine and puts them into practice is like a wise man who built his house on the rock. (Matthew 7:24, NIV)

Command them to do good, to be rich in good deeds, and to be generous and willing to share. In this way they will lay up treasure for themselves as a firm foundation for the coming age, so that they may take hold of the life that is truly life. (Timothy 6:18–19, NIV)

This service that you perform is not only supplying the needs of God's people but is also overflowing in many expressions of thanks to God. (Corinthians 9:12, NIV)

Because of the service by which you have proved yourselves, men will praise God for the obedience that accompanies your confession of the gospel of Christ, and for your generosity in sharing with them and with everyone else. (2 Corinthians 9:13, NIV)

I love the honesty of the "I Like Thinking and Doing" story, and I couldn't agree more: "The doing makes the thinking more fun." In fact, the Matthew 7:24 passage touches on this very point. It's at the end of the Sermon on the Mount. Jesus finishes His teaching by essentially saying "Now go do this stuff! Put it into practice!"

At the beginning of the book of Acts, Jesus' disciples watch Him ascend into heaven. There's actually a comical moment when an angel appears and says, "Men of Galilee, why do you stand here looking into the sky?" It's as if the angel says, "Okay. Go. Get busy. You've got stuff to do. He's taught you this life. He'll be back. In the meantime, you know exactly what to do. Now go! Do it!" And they did. They stopped looking into the sky and turned their focus to the world around them. They went to work, putting into practice all He'd taught them, and it changed the world. I'm convinced that if we put into practice the things we've discussed here, it will change us, it will change the people we serve, and—as it becomes a lifestyle—it will change the cultures we inhabit.

ACT

What can your group do together to give of yourselves to a person or persons in your community? Together brainstorm a project your group can carry forward from this study, one that puts into action your new discovery of the generous life.

A Final Note

As you continue your journey into the generous life, know that generous people need other generous people around them. I Like Giving is a fellow traveler on the path. Feel free to visit www.ilikegiving.com to keep viewing and reading inspiring stories of generosity.

Share your own story! Your experience of giving or receiving can help others. Post your story, and read others', at ilikegiving.com. Find I Like Giving on Facebook, Twitter, and Instagram to be inspired toward the generous life every day.

To get in touch with I Like Giving or to invite Brad to speak, contact info@ilikegiving.com. Thank you for joining us in discovering the joy of giving!

Learn how to bring the experience of generosity into your work, your church, ministry, and school at ilikegiving.com/get-involved.

Find more stories and short films of generosity online at ilikegiving.com.

Notes — Session 1

Notes — Session 2

Notes — Session 3

Notes — Session 4

Additional Notes